Mum and Dad painted the kitchen. Dad painted the ceiling. Mum painted the walls.

Mum pulled up the old carpet.
"The walls look good," she said. "But this looks a mess."

Dad looked at the floor. “We need a new carpet,” said Biff.

Mum found a trap door. She pulled it up.

Everyone looked.

"It's a cellar," said Dad.

Mum went into the cellar.
“It looks big,” she said.

The children looked in.
“It looks dark,” said Biff.
“It looks spooky,” said Chip.

Dad got a light. They went into the cellar.

Kipper found an old sheet.
"I'm a ghost," he said.
"Whoooooooooooooaa...!"

“Look at this,” said Kipper.
“What is it?” asked Chip.

“I don’t know,” said Mum.
“It’s a whatsit,” said Dad.

Wilf and Wilma came to play. They looked at the whatsit.
"What is it?" asked Wilma.

“It’s a whatsit,” said Chip.
“We found it in the cellar.”

Two men came to the house. They came in a lorry. They took away the old things.

One man looked at the whatsit.
"What is it?" he asked.
"It's a whatsit," said Dad.

The men took the whatsit. They put it in a lorry. A car stopped.

A lady jumped out and called to the men.
"Stop!" she said.

The lady wanted the whatsit. She wanted it for a museum. The men put it in the car.

The lady gave Dad some money.
“Come to the museum,” she said, “and bring the children.”

The whatsit was in the museum. Mum and Dad went to see it.

They took Biff, Chip and Kipper.
"So that's what it is," said Dad.

Mum and Dad had a surprise. It was for the children.
“What is it?” asked Biff.

“It’s a whatsit,” said Dad. He pulled off the sheet.

The whatsit was a snooker table.
“It’s brilliant!” they said.